GuestSpot

CHRISTMAS
Playalong *for* Clarinet

WISE PUBLICATIONS
London/New York/Paris/Sydney/Copenhagen/Madrid

Exclusive Distributors:
Music Sales Limited
8/9 Frith Street, London W1V 5TZ, England.
Music Sales Pty Limited
120 Rothschild Avenue, Rosebery, NSW 2018, Australia.

Order No. AM950422
ISBN 0-7119-7026-2
This book © Copyright 1997 by Wise Publications.

Book design by Michael Bell Design.
Music arranged by Jack Long.
Music processed by Enigma Music Production Services.
Cover photography by George Taylor.

CD recorded by Paul Honey.
Instrumental solos by John Whelan.
All keyboards and programming by Paul Honey.

Your Guarantee of Quality:
As publishers, we strive to produce every book to
the highest commercial standards.
The music has been freshly engraved and the book has been
carefully designed to minimise awkward page turns and
to make playing from it a real pleasure.
Particular care has been given to specifying acid-free, neutral-sized
paper made from pulps which have not been elemental chlorine bleached.
This pulp is from farmed sustainable forests and was
produced with special regard for the environment.
Throughout, the printing and binding have been planned to
ensure a sturdy, attractive publication which should give years of enjoyment.
If your copy fails to meet our high standards,
please inform us and we will gladly replace it.

Music Sales' complete catalogue describes thousands of
titles and is available in full colour sections by subject,
direct from Music Sales Limited.
Please state your areas of interest and send a
cheque/postal order for £1.50 for postage to:
Music Sales Limited, Newmarket Road, Bury St. Edmunds, Suffolk IP33 3YB.

Fingering Guide

Transposition

The Bb clarinet sounds a major second below the written pitch.

Rule: Written C sounds Bb

Written

Sounds

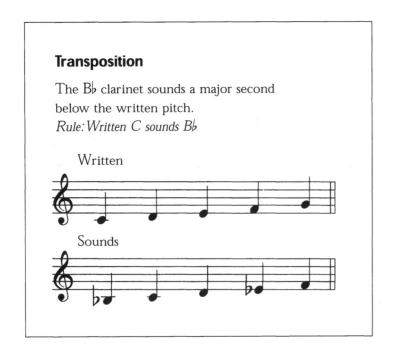

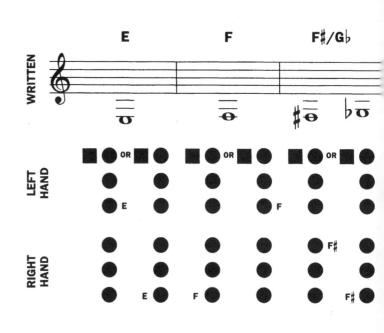

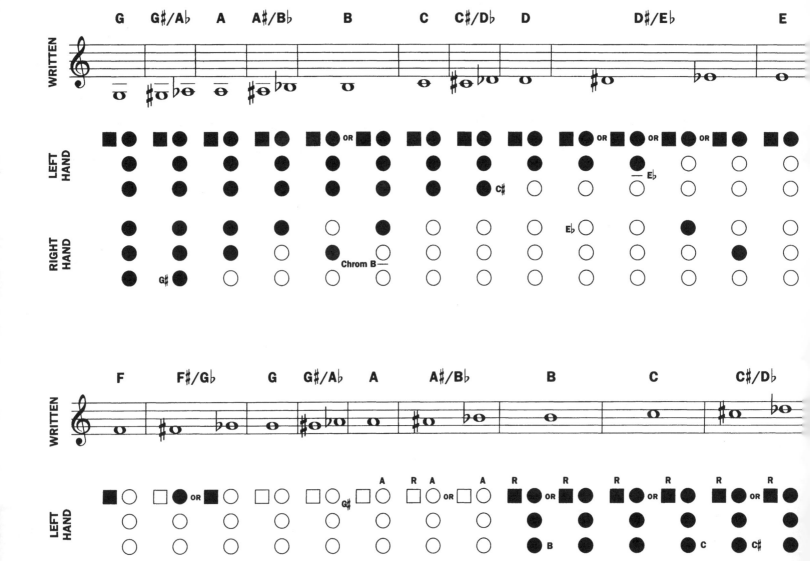

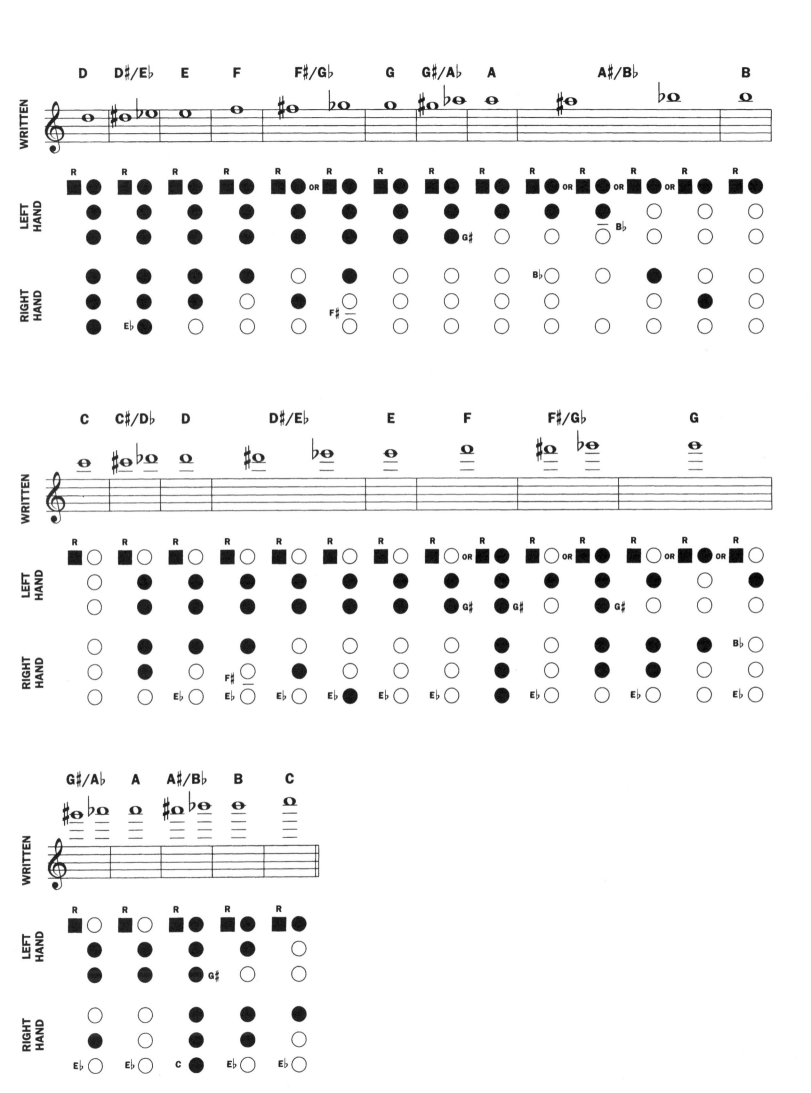

Frosty The Snowman

Words & Music by Steve Nelson & Jack Rollins

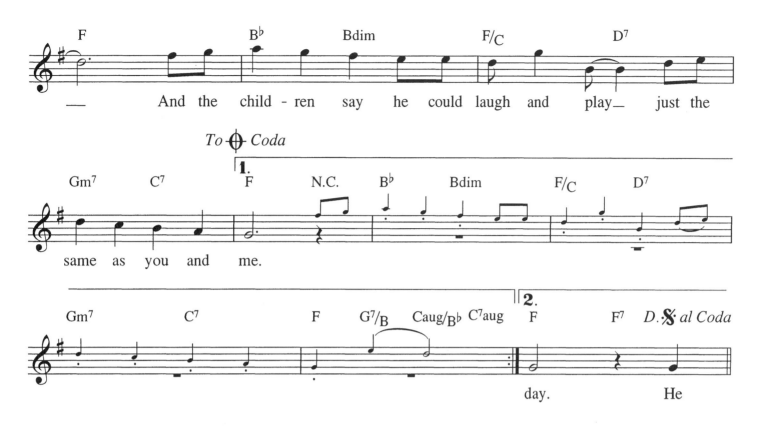

And the child-ren say he could laugh and play— just the same as you and me.

To ⊕ Coda

1.

day.   He

2.

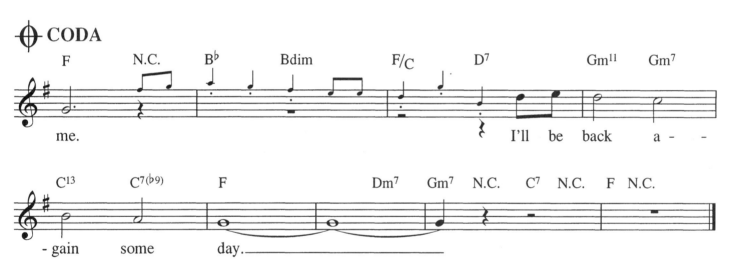

⊕ CODA

me.   I'll be back a - -

- gain   some   day.___

Verse 2
Frosty the Snowman knew the sun was hot that day,
So he said "Let's run, and we'll have some fun
Now before I melt away".
Down to the village, with a broomstick in his hand,
Running here and there all around the square,
Saying "Catch me if you can".
He led them down the streets of town
Right to the traffic cop,
And he only paused a moment when
He heard him holler "Stop!".
Frosty the Snowman had to hurry on his way,
But he waved goodbye, saying "Don't you cry,
I'll be back again some day".

Hark, The Herald Angels Sing

Christmas Carol

1. Hark, the her - ald

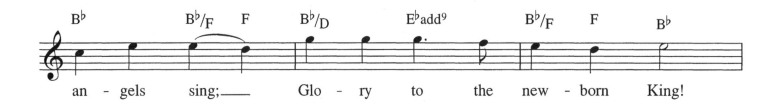

an - gels sing;____ Glo - ry to the new - born King!

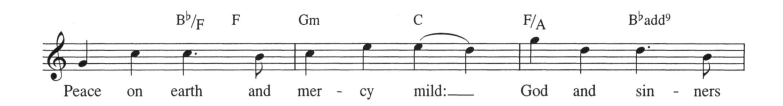

Peace on earth and mer - cy mild:____ God and sin - ners

re - con - ciled. Joy - ful, all ye na - tions rise,____

Join the tri - umph of the skies.____ With the'an - gel - ic host pro - claim:

'Christ is____ born in Beth - le - hem'. Hark, the her - ald

an - gels sing; Glo - ry___ to the new - born King!

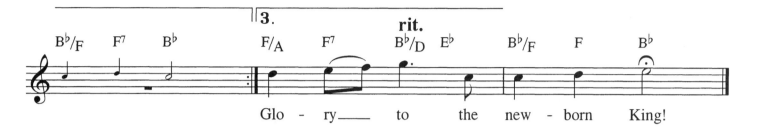

Glo - ry___ to the new - born King!

Verse 2
Christ, by highest Heav'n adored;
Christ, the everlasting Lord:
Late in time, behold him come,
Offspring of a Virgin's womb.
Veiled in flesh, the Godhead see!
Hail the incarnate Deity!
Pleased as man with man to dwell,
Jesus our Emmanuel!
Hark, the herald angels sing;
Glory to the new-born King!

Verse 3
Hail, the Heaven-born Prince of peace!
Hail the son of righteousness!
Light and life to all He brings,
Risen with healing in his wings.
Mild, He lays his glory by;
Born that man no more may die.
Born to raise the sons of earth;
Born to give them second birth.
Hark, the herald angels sing;
Glory to the new-born King!

Have Yourself A Merry Little Christmas

Words & Music by Hugh Martin & Ralph Blane

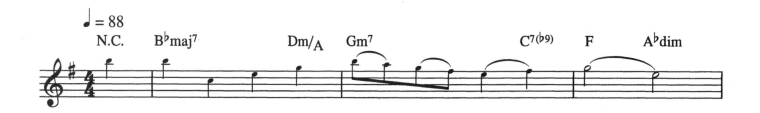

Have your-self a mer-ry lit-tle Christ-mas, let your heart be

light; Next year all our trou-bles will be out of sight.

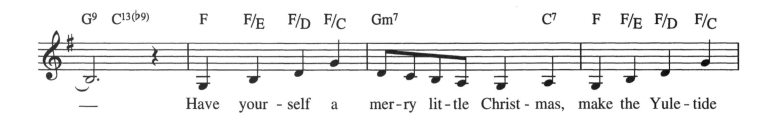

Have your-self a mer-ry lit-tle Christ-mas, make the Yule-tide

gay. Next year all our trou-bles will be miles a - way.

Once a-gain, as in old-en days, hap-py gold-en days of

yore, Faith - ful friends who are dear to us will be near to us once

more. Some - day soon we all will be to - geth - er, if the fates al -

- low. Un - til then, we'll have to mud - dle through some - how.____

____ So have your - self a mer - ry lit - tle Christ - mas now.____

CODA   **Slower**

- how._____ So have your - self a

mer - ry lit - tle Christ - mas now._____

Jingle Bells

Traditional

Jin - gle bells, jin - gle bells, jin - gle all the

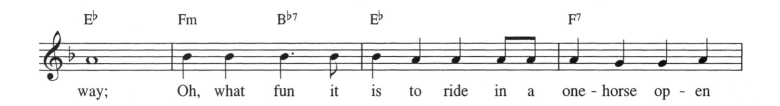

way; Oh, what fun it is to ride in a one - horse op - en

sleigh. Jin - gle bells, jin - gle bells, jin - gle all the

way; Oh, what fun it is to ride in a one - horse op - en

sleigh. 1. Dash - ing through the snow in a
(Verse 2 see block lyric)

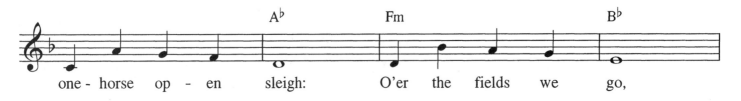

one - horse op - en sleigh: O'er the fields we go,

laugh - ing all the way. Bells on bob - tail ring,

mak - ing spi - rits bright: What fun it is to ride and sing a

sleigh - ing song to - night. Jin - gle bells, jin - gle bells,

jin - gle all the way; Oh, what fun it is to ride in a

one - horse op - en sleigh. Jin - gle bells, jin - gle bells,

jin - gle all the way; Oh, what fun it is to ride in a

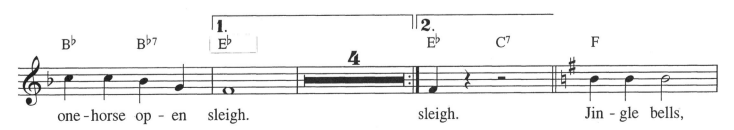

one-horse op - en sleigh. sleigh. Jin - gle bells,

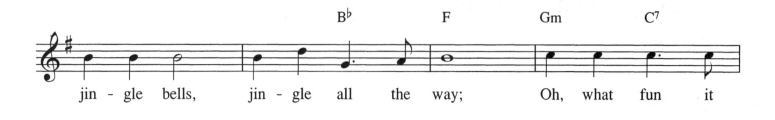

jin - gle bells,   jin - gle all the way;   Oh, what fun it

is to ride in a one - horse op - en sleigh.   Jin - gle bells,

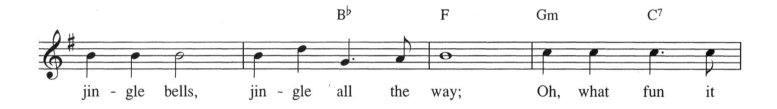

jin - gle bells,   jin - gle all the way;   Oh, what fun it

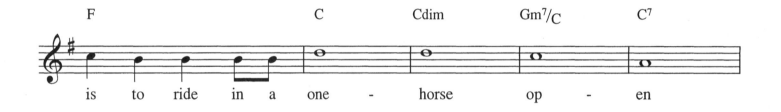

is to ride in a one - horse op - en

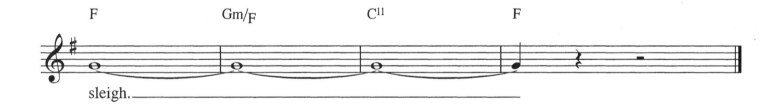

sleigh.

Verse 2
Now the ground is white, go it while you're young;
Take the girls tonight, sing this sleighing song.
Get a bob-tailed bay, two-forty for his speed;
Then hitch him to an open sleigh,
And you will take the lead.

Mary's Boy Child

Words & Music by Jester Hairston

Calypso ($\quad = 100$)

Long

time a-go___ in Beth-le-hem,___ so the Ho-ly Bi-ble say,___

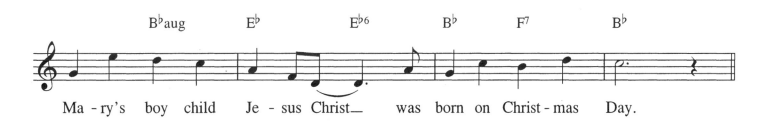

Ma-ry's boy child Je-sus Christ___ was born on Christ-mas Day.

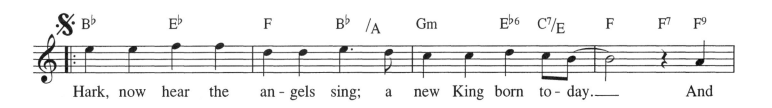

Hark, now hear the an-gels sing; a new King born to-day.___ And

Man will live for ev-er-more,___ Be-cause of Christ-mas Day.

Trum-pets sound and an-gels sing, lis-ten to what they say:___ That

Man will live for ev - er - more,— Be - cause of Christ - mas Day.

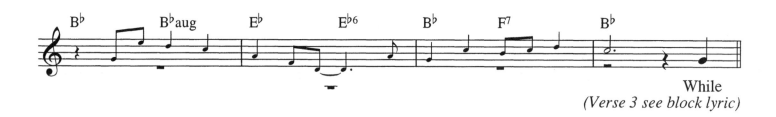

While
(Verse 3 see block lyric)

shep - herds watched— their flocks by night,— them see a bright new shin - ing star._

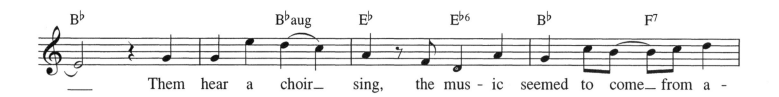

_ Them hear a choir_ sing, the mus - ic seemed to come_ from a -

- far. Now Jo - seph and_ his wife, Ma - ry,_ come to

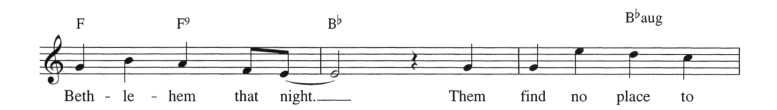

Beth - le - hem that night._ Them find no place to

D. %· al Coda

born she child,_ Not a sin - gle room_ was in sight. Day.

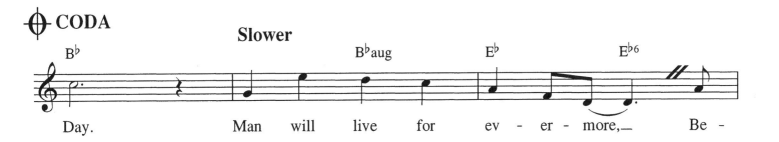

CODA

Slower

Day. Man will live for ev - er - more,— Be -

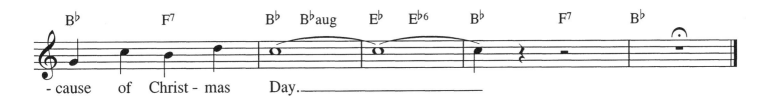

- cause of Christ - mas Day.

Verse 3
By and by they find a little nook
In a stable all forlorn;
And, in a manger cold and dark,
Mary's little boy was born.
Long time ago in Bethlehem,
So the Holy Bible say,
Mary's boy child, Jesus Christ,
Was born on Christmas Day.

O Little Town Of Bethlehem

Traditional Christmas Carol

1. O

lit - tle town of Beth - le - hem, how still we__ see thee

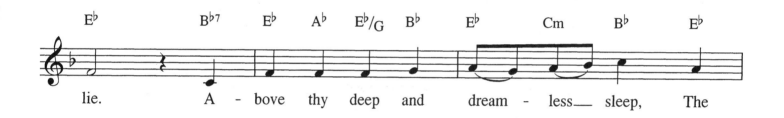

lie. A - bove thy deep and dream - less__ sleep, The

si - lent__ stars go by. Yet__ in thy dark__ streets__

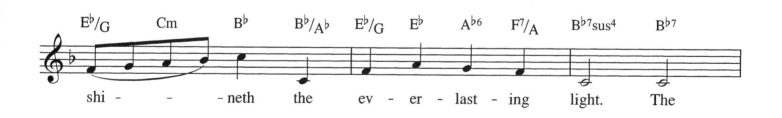

shi - - -neth the ev - er - last - ing light. The

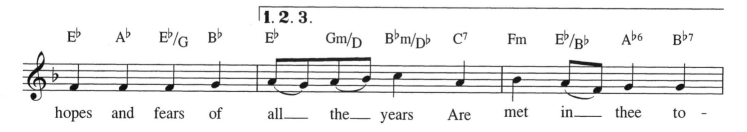

hopes and fears of all__ the__ years Are met in__ thee to -

night.

2. O

- bide___ with___ us,   our   Lord   Em - ma - nu - el!

Verse 2

O morning stars, together proclaim the holy birth;
And praises sing to God the King,
And peace to men on earth.
For Christ is born of Mary and, gathered all above
While mortals sleep, the angels keep
Their watch of wond'ring love.

Verse 3

How silently, how silently, the wond'rous gift is given!
So God imparts to human hearts
The blessings of His Heaven.
No ear may hear his coming; but, in this world of sin,
Where meek souls will receive Him still
The dear Christ enters in.

Verse 4

O holy child of Bethlehem, descend to us we pray;
Cast out our sin and enter in,
Be born in us today.
We hear the Christmas angels the great good tidings tell.
O come to us, abide with us,
Our Lord Emmanuel!

Once In Royal David's City

Traditional Christmas Carol

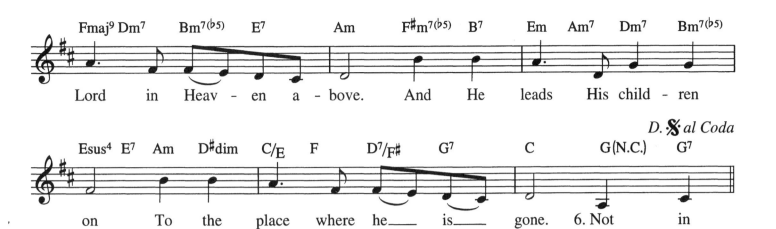

Lord in Heav - en a - bove. And He leads His child - ren

D. %‌ al Coda

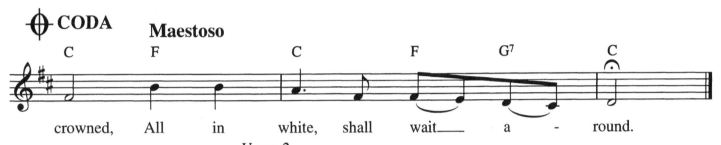

on To the place where he___ is___ gone. 6. Not in

⊕ CODA   **Maestoso**

C	F		C	F	G⁷	C

crowned, All in white, shall wait___ a - round.

Verse 2
He came down to earth from Heaven,
Who is God and Lord of all;
And His shelter was a stable,
And His cradle was a stall.
With the poor and meek and lowly,
Lived on earth our Saviour holy.

Verse 3
And, through all his wond'rous childhood,
He would honour and obey,
Love and watch the lowly maiden
In whose gentle arms He lay,
Christian children all must be
Mild, obedient, good as He.

Verse 4
For He is our childhood's pattern,
Day by day, like us, He grew.
He was little, weak and helpless;
Tears and smiles, like us, He knew.
And He feeleth for our sadness,
And He shareth in our gladness.

Verse 5
See music.

Verse 6
Not in that poor lowly stable,
With the oxen standing by,
We shall see Him, but in Heaven,
Set at God's right hand on high:
When, like stars, His children, crowned
All in white, shall wait around.

Silent Night

Words & Music by Joseph Mohr & Franz Gruber

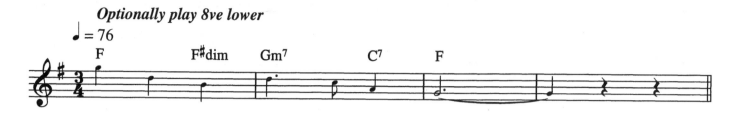

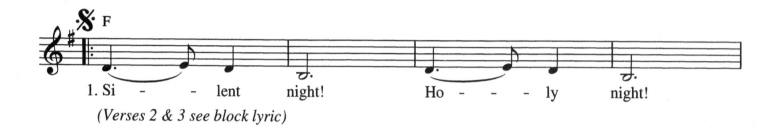

1. Si - - lent night! Ho - - ly night!

(Verses 2 & 3 see block lyric)

All is calm, all is bright

Round yon Vir - - gin and_____ her child.

Ho - - ly In - fant, so ten - der and mild,

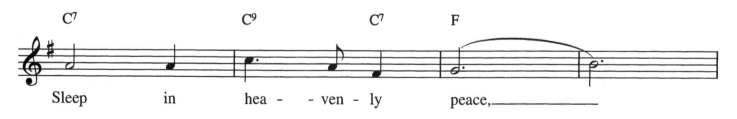

Sleep in hea - - ven - ly peace,_____

CODA

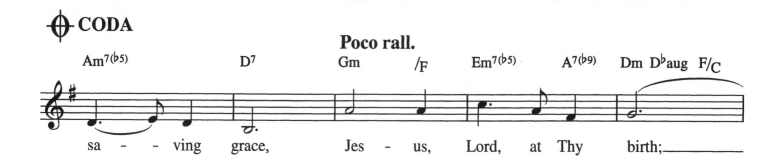

Poco rall.

| Am7(♭5) | D7 | Gm | /F | Em7(♭5) | A7(♭9) | Dm D♭aug F/C |

sa - - ving grace, Jes - us, Lord, at Thy birth;_____

a tempo, slower

| Bm7(♭5) | F/C | F#dim Gm7 | C7 | F |

____ Jes - - us, Lord, at Thy birth!_____

Verse 2
Silent night! Holy night!
Shepherds quail at the sight.
Glories stream from Heaven afar;
Heavenly hosts sing Alleluia!
Christ the Saviour is born,
Christ the Saviour is born.

Verse 3
Tacet

Verse 4
Silent night! Holy night!
Son of God, loves pure light:
Radiant beams Thy holy face
With the dawn of saving grace,
Jesus, Lord, at Thy birth;
Jesus, Lord, at Thy birth!

Sleigh Ride

Words by Mitchell Parish
Music by Leroy Anderson

CODA

Molto rall.

you.

Verse 2
Outside the snow is falling and friends are calling "Yoo, hoo!";
Come on, it's lovely weather for a sleigh ride together with you.

Verse 4
Let's take that road before us and sing a chorus or two;
Come on, it's lovely weather for a sleigh ride together with you.

Verse 6
There's a happy feeling nothing in the world can buy,
When they pass around the coffee and the pumpkin pie;
It'll nearly be like a picture print by Currier and Ives.
These wonderful things are the things
We remember all through our lives!

Winter Wonderland

Words by Dick Smith
Music by Felix Bernard

Optionally play 8ve lower

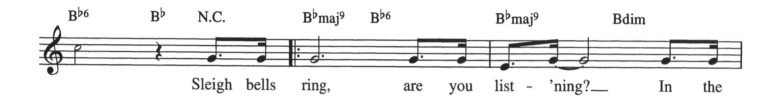

Sleigh bells ring, are you list - 'ning?___ In the

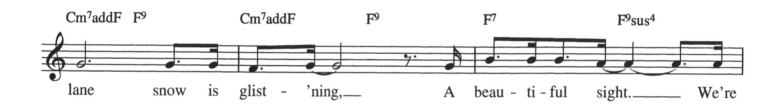

lane snow is glist - 'ning,___ A beau - ti - ful sight.___ We're

hap - py to - night___ walk - ing in a win - ter won - der - land.___ Gone a -

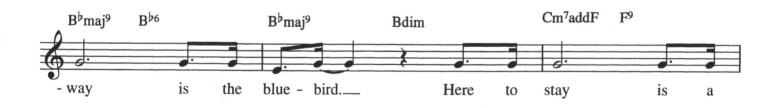

- way is the blue - bird.___ Here to stay is a

new bird:___ He sings a love - song___ as we go a - long,___

10/07 (63775)